Sticky the Kitt

Coloring and Activity Book

(That means you can draw all over it!)

A nice thing to do for someone is...

(Draw a nice thing to do for someone)

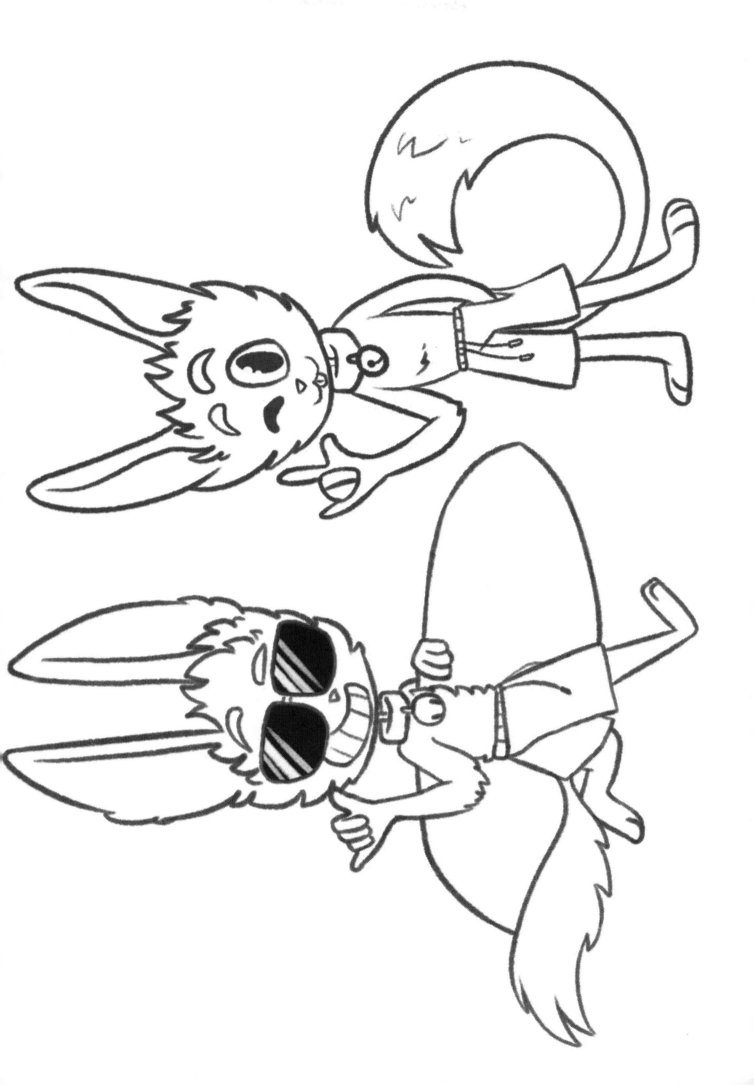

If a kitten needed help, I would...

(Draw how you would help a kitten)

My favorite picture of Sticky is...

(Draw your favorite picture of Sticky)

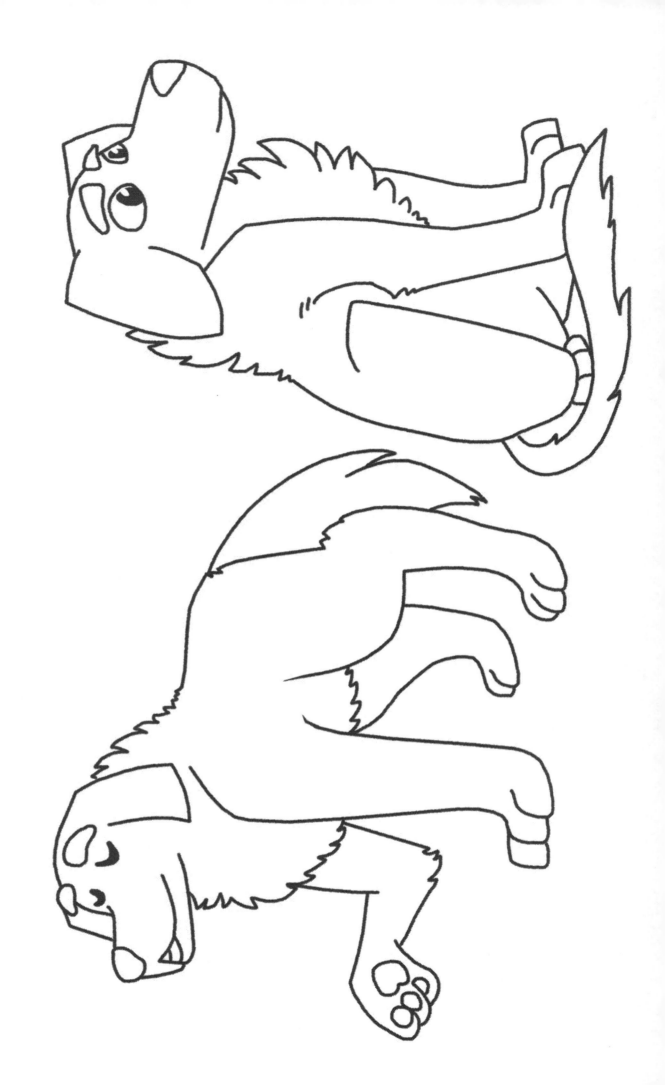

Something that makes me happy is...

(Draw something that makes you happy)

Something that makes me smile is...

(Draw something that makes you smile)

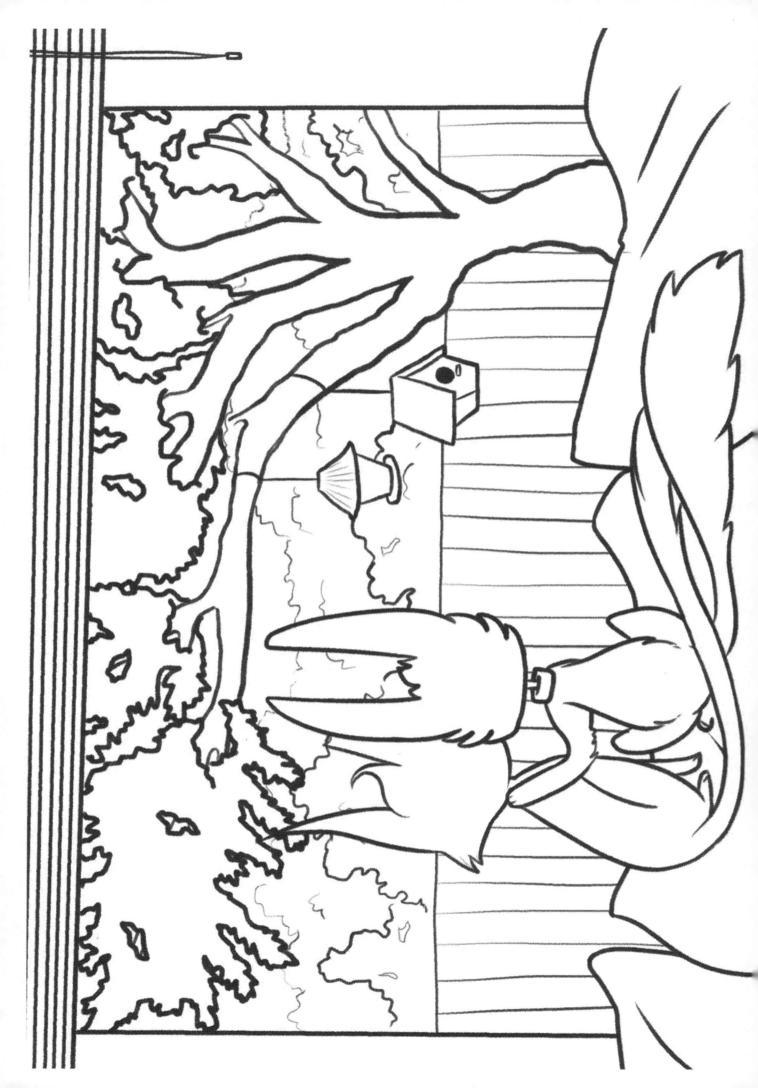

Made in the USA
Middletown, DE
31 October 2020

23081208R00018